eckle, FEED, persecute, irk, ve... ...se,
e DO NOT annoy, pester, tormen... ...le,
shout at the animals! Thank yo... ...NOT
ecute, irk, vex, bother, tease, frighten or shout at
ster, torment, harass, heckle, FEED, persecute,
imals! Thank you. Please DO NOT annoy, pester,
bother, tease, frighten or shout at the animals!
harass, heckle, FEED, persecute, irk, vex, bother,
Please DO NOT annoy, pester, torment, harass,
frighten or shout at the animals! Thank you.

Please **DO NOT**
annoy, pester, torment,
plague, molest, worry,
badger, harry, harass,
heckle, feed, persecute,
irk, vex, bother, tease,
nettle, ruffle, irritate,
frighten, or shout at
the animals!

Thank you.

**LONDON ZOO**
CONSERVATION · ACTION

# PLEASE DO NOT FEED...

Andy Morley-Hall

spine

WHERE AM I?

I hide among the
rocks to escape
from the heat.

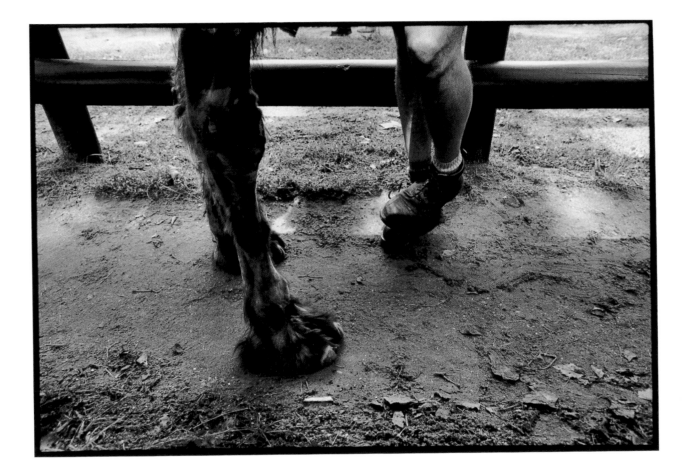

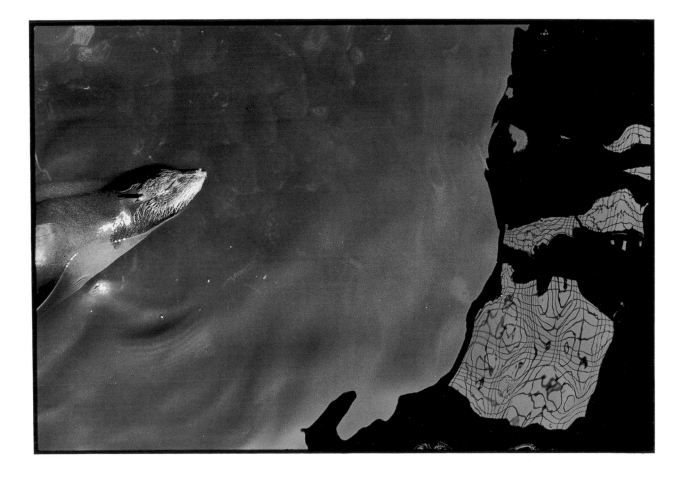

Please DO NOT
annoy, pester, torment,
plague, molest, worry,
badger, harry, harass,
heckle, feed, persecute,
irk, vex, bother, tease,
nettle, ruffle, irritate,
frighten, or shout at
the animals!

Thank you.

LONDON ZOO
CONSERVATION • ACTION

**Annoy**  *an·noy v*
1. *vt* to make somebody feel impatient or angry
2. *vt* to harass or bother somebody repeatedly
3. *vi* to be a source of irritation

**Pester**  *pes·ter vt*
to be a constant source of annoyance to somebody,
for example, by harassing him or her with demands

**Torment**  *tor·ment vt*
1. to inflict torture, pain or anguish on somebody
or something
2. to tease a person or an animal persistently
3. to severely distort, twist or wrench something (archaic
or literary)
*n*
1. severe mental anguish or physical pain
2. a source of severe mental anguish or physical pain
3. a source of annoyance or anxiety

**Plague**  *plague n*
1. a disease that spreads very rapidly, infecting very large
numbers of people and killing a great many of them, or an
outbreak of such a disease
2. the bubonic plague
3. the appearance of something harmful or annoying such as

vermin in abnormally large numbers, or with abnormal
frequency
4. an affliction or extremely troublesome or annoying
person or thing
*vt*
1. to occur or recur frequently, causing a great deal of
trouble, difficulty or pain to somebody or something (often
passive)
2. to harass or annoy somebody constantly, usually by
asking questions or making requests or demands

**Molest**  *mo·lest vt*
1. to force unwanted sexual attentions on somebody,
especially a child or physically weaker adult (disapproving)
2. to pester, bother or disturb a person or animal

**Worry**  *wor·ry v*
1. *vti* to feel anxious or to cause another person to
feel anxious about something unpleasant that may
have happened or may happen
2. *vt* to annoy another person by making insistent
demands or complaints
3. *vt* to try to wound or kill an animal by biting it
4. *vt* See worry at
5. *vi* to proceed persistently despite problems or obstacles
6. *vt* to touch, move or interfere with something repeatedly

*n*

1. a feeling of anxiety or concern
2. something that causes anxiety or concern
3. a period spent feeling anxious or concerned

**Badger**  *badg·er n*

a medium-sized burrowing animal that is related to the weasel and has short legs, strong claws, and a thick coat. It usually has black and white stripes on the sides of its head. Subfamily: Melinae

*vt*

to pester or annoy somebody continually

**Harry**  *har·ry or har·row (archaic) vt*

1. to cause somebody mental, emotional or physical distress by repeated verbal or physical attacks
2. to raid or pillage an area, or a town or village, especially during a war

**Harass**  *ha·rass vt*

1. to persistently annoy, attack or bother somebody
2. to exhaust an enemy by repeatedly attacking

**Heckle**  *heck·le v*

1. *vti* to shout remarks, insults or questions in order to disconcert somebody who is making a speech

or giving a performance

2. *vt* to comb flax or hemp

*n*

a comb used for dressing flax or hemp

**Feed**  *feed v*

1. *vt* to give food to a person or an animal
2. *vt* to give something as food to a person or an animal
3. *vt* to serve as or be enough food for a person or an animal
4. *vi* to eat food or take in nourishment
5. *vt* to sustain or encourage a specific belief or behaviour
6. *vt* to provide the necessary materials for something to operate
7. *vti* to move something gradually into, through or out of something, or be moved in this way
8. *vt* to deliver a line or cue to a fellow performer
9. *vti* to pass a ball to a teammate (informal)
10. *vt* to supply power or an electrical signal to a system, component or station
11. *vti* to provide a local television or radio broadcast to a larger audience by using a satellite or network

*n*

1. an act or occasion of feeding
2. food, especially for animals or babies
3. a meal, especially a large and satisfying one (dated informal)
4. a device that supplies material to a machine, as does the

paper tray on a printer
5. the signal a network broadcasts to local radio
or television stations for broadcast
6. somebody who delivers a line or cue to a fellow
performer

**Persecute**  *per·se·cute vt*
1. to systematically subject a race or group of people to
cruel or unfair treatment, for example, because of their ethnic
origin or religious beliefs
2. to make somebody the victim of continual pestering or
harassment

**Irk**  *irk vt*
to annoy somebody slightly, especially by being tedious

**Vex**
1. to make somebody annoyed or upset
2. to cause somebody anxiety or distress
3. to confuse or puzzle somebody

**Bother**  *both·er v*
1. *vi* to take the time or trouble to do something (often
used in negative statements)
2. *vti* to make somebody feel worried, anxious or upset
3. *vt* to annoy or disturb somebody, for example, by

interrupting or by making unwelcome advances
4. *vt* to make somebody feel physical discomfort or pain
*n*
1. trouble or effort to do something
2. somebody or something that causes annoyance, for
example, by making noise

**Tease**  *tease v*
1. *vti* to deliberately annoy or irritate a person or an animal
2. *vti* to make fun of somebody, either playfully or maliciously
3. *vt* to urge somebody, especially to do something, by
continual coaxing
4. *vt* to arouse hope, curiosity or especially physical desire
in somebody with no intention of giving satisfaction
5. *vt* to comb the hair with quick short movements toward
the roots so that it stands up away from the head
6. *vt* to pull fibres apart by combing or carding
7. *vt* to raise the nap on cloth by combing it with a wire brush
8. *vt* to separate the parts of a tissue specimen gently with
a needle in preparation for examination under a microscope
*n*
1. a person who has a tendency to tease others; also called teaser
2. a person who teases somebody else sexually
3. an opening remark or action intended to stimulate
curiosity or interest
4. an act of teasing

**Nettle**   *net·tle n*
1. a wild plant with serrated-edged leaves that are covered with fine hairs or spines that sting when touched.
Genus: *Urtica*
Also called stinging nettle
2. a wild plant with serrated leaves like a stinging nettle, but without the stinging hairs, especially a deadnettle.
Genus: *Lamium*
*vt*
1. to irritate or annoy somebody (informal)
2. to sting somebody

**Ruffle**   *ruf·fle1 v*
1. *vti* to disturb or ripple something, especially a surface, or to become disturbed or rippled
2. *vt* to erect feathers, for example, in defence, as a display or for warmth or grooming
3. *vti* to bother or fluster somebody, or to become bothered or flustered
4. *vt* to flip rapidly through the pages of a book or magazine (dated)
5. *vt* to draw a strip of material into pleats or gathers to use as trim
6. *vt* to shuffle playing cards (dated)
*n*
1. a disturbance or ripple in something, especially a surface
2. a source of irritation or annoyance
3. a strip of closely pleated or gathered material used as trim

**Irritate**   *ir·ri·tate v*
1. *vti* to cause somebody to feel annoyance or exasperation, or cause annoyance or exasperation
2. *vt* to stimulate a body part excessively, causing a painful reaction, for example, inflammation
3. *vt* to stimulate an organism so as to provoke a response

**Frighten**   *fright·en v*
1. *vti* to make somebody feel fear or to be made to feel fear
2. *vt* to force or drive somebody or something away through fear

**Shout**   *shout v*
1. *vt* to say or utter something very loudly
2. *vi* to speak in a loud or angry voice
3. *vti* Australia, New Zealand: to buy something for somebody else, especially a drink in a bar or a meal in a restaurant (informal)
*n*
1. a loud call or cry
2. Australia, New Zealand, UK: somebody's turn to buy something, especially a drink or meal (informal)

First published in Great Britain in 2003 by
Spine Publishing
23 Nassau Street, London W1W 7AG

ISBN 0 9544031 1 8

Originated, printed and bound in Italy by Graphicom Srl

The photographs in this book are reproduced by permission of the following zoos.

Bristol Zoo: photographs on pages 31 (seals); 39 (fish from below); 51 (flying penguin); 93 (Dr Seuss seal).

Chester Zoo: photographs on pages 9 (girl & monkey); 17 (penguin statue); 19 (photocall for amorous turtles); 21 (girl reaching for fish); 69 (monkey, blonde hair); 73 (chimpanzee in sunlight); 87 (zebra & fence); 91 (chimpanzee & high walls).

London Zoo: photographs on front cover & page 59 (penguin & scarf); and on pages 1 & 98 (London Zoo sign); 5 (pushing rhino); 7 (tiger balloon); 11 (sheep & elephant); 13 (photographer & tiger); 15 ('Where am I?'); 19 (hoovering stage); 23 (penguins & hose); 25 (pelicans); 27 (snakes & branches); 29 (girl & lions); 33 (beetle, feet); 35 (giraffe, toy lion); 37 (deflated giraffe); 41 (tiger, fur coat); 43 (camel's legs & man's); 45 (girl & owl); 49 (giraffe, split neck); 53 (okapi & kebab); 55 (elephant kiss); 57 (toy snake & eagle); 61 (elephant trunk, shadows); 63 (girl on wall, bird); 65 (sheep & dinosaur); 67 (lion, hand); 71 (pelican feeding time); 75 (windowcleaner); 77 (headband & shorts at gorilla cage); 79 (lion ignoring onlooker); 81 (girls & tiger); 83 (zebra, girl in heels); 85 ('Zoo staff only'); 89 (rhino, tripod-man); 95 (hornbill, hat-man); 97 (heron over penguin pond).

Consultant editor: Paul Forty
Production: Martin Lee
Typography and layout: Paul Martin
Prints: Andy Walsh at Potosi
Photograph selection and sequencing: Jamie Colonna, Matthew Stuart and Nick Turpin

Please DO NOT annoy, pester, torment, harass, frighten or shout at the animals! Thank you. Plea FEED, persecute, irk, vex, bother, tease, frighten annoy, pester, torment, harass, heckle, FEED, pe the animals! Thank you. Please DO NOT annoy, irk, vex, bother, tease, frighten or shout at the torment, harass, heckle, FEED, persecute, irk, v Thank you. Please DO NOT annoy, pester, tormen tease, frighten or shout at the animals! Thank y heckle, FEED, persecute, irk, vex, bother, tea